The Box

by Jane Simon

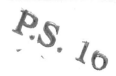

Harcourt

Orlando   Boston   Dallas   Chicago   San Diego

Visit *The Learning Site!*

www.harcourtschool.com

I will make a box.

Is it a box of cats?

Don't look, Pa!

Is it a box of socks?

Don't look, Pa!

Is it a box of tops?

Don't you like it?